A VERY BRAVE Witch

Alison McGHEE

Harry BLISS

SCHOLASTIC INC.

New York Toronto London Auckland Sydney
Mexico City New Delhi Hong Kong Buenos Aires

ISBN-13: 978-0-545-05385-3
ISBN-10: 0-545-05385-4

12 11 10 9 8 7 6 5 4 3 2 1   7 8 9 10 11 12/0

Printed in the U.S.A.   08

First Scholastic printing, October 2007

Book design by Einav Aviram
Hand lettering by Paul Colin
The illustrations for this book are rendered in black ink and watercolor
on Arches 90 lb. watercolor paper.

To Holly McGhee—A. M.

For Charley and Ben Bliss—H. B.

Most humans do not wear pointy hats.

Humans are rarely known to cackle.

HA, HA, HA, HA

Nothing too bad, except, you know... the green thing.